This book belongs to

_____

_____

_____

Victoria

MORNING GLORIES

Journal of a Year

Victoria

Morning Glories

Journal of a Year

Foreword

Ann's birthday, Susan's Valentine Party, John's graduation, and the evensong of church—all are dates I must remember, and what better way than with a beautiful book to remind me of the important days of my year.

We have called this journal of a year "Morning Glories" because each day rises as this flower does, gentle and full of promise. We hope that as you turn this book's pages, filling the white spaces with notations of your own memories, you will have a lovely and lasting record of your own beautiful year.

Nancy Lindemeyer
Victoria

J

J A N U A R Y

1

NEW YEAR'S DAY

2

3

4

5

6

In the midst of winter, I finally learned
that there was in me an invincible summer.

ALBERT CAMUS

J A N U A R Y

7

8

9

10

11

12

Winter is the time for comfort,
for good food and warmth, for the touch
of a friendly hand and for a talk
beside the fire: it is the time for home.

EDITH SITWELL

J A N U A R Y

13

14

15

16

17

18

The beauty of an ice storm is the glittering beauty of diamonds and rubies, of sapphires, topaz and emeralds—an Amazon wearing all her jewels; the beauty of snow on ice is the beauty of old lace—a grand dame in billows of rose point and Valenciennes.

RICHARDSON WRIGHT

J

J A N U A R Y

19

20

21

22

23

24

We looked upon a world unknown,
On nothing we could call our own.
Around the glistening wonder bent
The blue walls of the firmament,
No cloud above, no earth below,—
A universe of sky and snow!

JOHN GREENLEAF WHITTIER

JANUARY

25

26

27

28

29

30 / 31

The frost performs its secret ministry,
Unhelped by any wind.

SAMUEL TAYLOR COLERIDGE

F

FEBRUARY

1

2

GROUNDHOG DAY

3

4

5

6

February, when the days of winter seem
endless and no amount of wistful recollecting
can bring back any air of summer. . . .

SHIRLEY JACKSON

F E B R U A R Y

7

8

9

10

11

12

LINCOLN'S BIRTHDAY

And Winter slumbering in the open air
Wears on her smiling face a dream of Spring.

ANONYMOUS

F E B R U A R Y

13

14

VALENTINE'S DAY

15

16

17

18

Nothing has happened today except kindness....

GERTRUDE STEIN

F

FEBRUARY

19

20

21

22

WASHINGTON'S BIRTHDAY

23

24

Out of the bosom of the Air,
Out of the cloud-folds of her garments shaken,
Over the woodlands, brown and bare,
Over the harvest fields forsaken,
Silent, and soft, and slow
Descends the snow.

HENRY WADSWORTH LONGFELLOW

F

FEBRUARY

25

26

27

28

. . . the lanterns picked out snow falling,
the bricks already covered with a flour dusting and
here and there a few footprints showing.

SUSAN MINOT

MARCH

1

2

3

4

5

6

It is the first mild day of March:
Each minute sweeter than before . . .
There is a blessing in the air. . . .

WILLIAM WORDSWORTH

MARCH

7

8

9

10

11

12

My heart is singing for joy this morning.
A miracle has happened!

ANNIE SULLIVAN

M

M A R C H

13

14

15

16

17

St. Patrick's Day

18

March is a tomboy with tousled
hair, a mischievous smile, mud on her
shoes and a laugh in her voice.

HAL BORLAND

M A R C H

19

20

21 *VERNAL EQUINOX*

22

23

24

Children hold spring so tightly
in their brown fists—
just as grownups, who are less sure of it,
hold it in their hearts.

E. B. WHITE

M
M A R C H

25

26

27

28

29

30/31

He had happened upon her one afternoon in the early spring, bending over the violets that grew along the side fence under the lilacs, turning back last autumn's leaves to show him and inviting him to share her pleasure.

HELEN HOOVEN SANTMYER

APRIL

1

APRIL FOOL'S DAY

2

3

4

5

6

Spring comes laughing down the valley
All in white, from the snow
Where the winter's armies rally
Loth to go.

APRIL

7

8

9

10

11

12

I know there will be spring; as surely as the
birds know it when they see above
the snow two tiny, quivering green leaves.
Spring cannot fail us.

OLIVE SCHREINER

APRIL

13

14

15

16

17

18

April, April,/Laugh thy girlish laughter;/
Then, the moment after,/Weep thy girlish tears!

SIR WILLIAM WATSON

APRIL

19

20

21

22

23

24

O the green things growing, the green things growing,
The faint sweet smell of the green things growing!

DINAH MULOCK CRAIK

APRIL

25

26

27

28

29

30

No Winter lasts forever, no Spring
skips its turn. April is a promise that May is
bound to keep, and we know it.

HAL BORLAND

M A Y

1

2

3

4

5

6

The world's favorite season is the spring.
All things seem possible in May.

EDWIN WAY TEALE

MAY

7

8

9

10

11

12

I have met with but one or two persons
in the course of my life who understood the
art of Walking, that is, of taking walks—who had
a genius, so to speak, for sauntering.

HENRY DAVID THOREAU

M A Y

13

14

15

16

17

18

Spring, Spring, beautiful Spring.

ELIZA COOK

M A Y

19

20

21

22

23

24

Spring rides no horses down the hill,
But comes on foot, a goose-girl still.
And all the loveliest things there be
Come simply so, it seems to me.

EDNA ST. VINCENT MILLAY

M A Y

25

26

27

28

29

30 / 31

The word May is a perfumed word. It is an illuminated initial.
It means youth, love, song, and all that is beautiful in life.

HENRY WADSWORTH LONGFELLOW

J

J U N E

1

2

3

4

5

6

Nothing is so lovely as Spring . . .
long and lovely and lush.

GERARD MANLEY HOPKINS

JUNE

7

8

9

10

11

12

The world is wide; not two days are alike, nor even two hours; neither was there ever two leaves of a tree alike since the creation of the world; and the genuine productions of art, like those of nature, are all distinct from each other.

JOHN CONSTABLE

J U N E

13

14

FLAG DAY

15

16

17

18

O Spring! I know thee.

ALICE MEYNELL

J U N E

19

20

21

Summer Solstice

22

23

24

I expect some new phases of
life this summer, and shall try to get the
honey from each moment.

LUCY STONE

J U N E

25	
26	
27	
28	
29	
30/31	

What is lovely never dies
But passes into other loveliness,
Star-dust, or sea foam, flower or winged air.

THOMAS BAILEY ALDRICH

J U L Y

1

2

3

4

Independence Day

5

6

Every flower is a soul blossoming out to nature.

GERARD DE NERVAL

J U L Y

7

8

9

10

11

12

Time flies,
Suns rise
And shadows fall.
Let time go by.
Love is forever over all.

ANONYMOUS

J U L Y

13

14

15

16

17

18

Summertime, oh, summertime,
pattern of life indelible, the fadeproof lake,
the woods unshatterable, the pasture
with the sweetfern and the juniper forever
and ever, summer without end. . . .

E. B. WHITE

J U L Y

19

20

21

22

23

24

Hot July brings cooling showers,
Apricots and gillyflowers.

SARA COLERIDGE

JULY

25

26

27

28

29

30/31

Nothing is worth more than this day.

JOHANN WOLFGANG VON GOETHE

A

A U G U S T

1

2

3

4

5

6

Complacencies of the peignoir, and late
Coffee and oranges in a sunny chair. . . .
The day is like wide water, without sound,
Stilled for passing of her dreaming feet. . . .

WALLACE STEVENS

AUGUST

7

8

9

10

11

12

I walk without flinching through the burning cathedral of the summer. My bank of wild grass is majestic and full of music. It is a fire that solitude presses against my lips.

VIOLETTE LEDUC

AUGUST

13

14

15

16

17

18

Inebriate of air—am I—
And Debauchee of Dew—
Reeling—through endless summer days—
From inns of Molten Blue—

EMILY DICKINSON

AUGUST

19

20

21

22

23

24

Gently Steep our Spirits,
Carrying with Them Dreams of Flowers.

WILLIAM WORDSWORTH

A U G U S T

25

26

27

28

29

30/31

"Do you go for a walk every morning?"

"Every morning."

"And what if the weather is bad?"

"Then I walk in bad weather."

COLETTE

S E P T E M B E R

1

2

3

4

5

6

Oh! For a book, and a cozy nook
And oh! For a quiet hour. . . .

ANONYMOUS

S E P T E M B E R

7

8

9

10

11

12

Strange what a difference a glorious day
can make! How one revels in life, in being, in poetry,
in the holy ridiculousness of things!

LIONEL JOHNSON

S E P T E M B E R

13

14

15

16

17

18

I'll tell you how the Sun rose—
A Ribbon at a time—

EMILY DICKINSON

SEPTEMBER

19

20

21

22

AUTUMNAL EQUINOX

23

24

Time is
Too slow for those who Wait
Too swift for those who Fear,
Too long for those who Grieve,
Too short for those who Rejoice;
But for those who Love
Time is
Eternity.

ANONYMOUS

SEPTEMBER

25

26

27

28

29

30

A nd yet," plied my friend, "nature has not changed. The night is still unsullied, the stars still twinkle, and the wild thyme smells as sweetly now as it did then.... We may be afflicted and unhappy, but no one can take from us the sweet delight which is nature's gift to those who love her and her poetry."

GEORGE SAND

OCTOBER

1

2

3

4

5

6

O suns and skies and flowers of June,
Count all your boasts together,
Love loveth best of all the year
October's bright blue weather.

HELEN HUNT JACKSON

OCTOBER

7

8

9

10

11

12

Be like the sun and the meadow,
which are not in the least concerned
about the coming winter.

GEORGE BERNARD SHAW

O C T O B E R

13

14

15

16

17

18

In Nature there is nothing melancholy.

SAMUEL TAYLOR COLERIDGE

OCTOBER

19

20

21

22

23

24

Autumnal frosts enchant the pool,
And make the cart ruts beautiful.

ROBERT LOUIS STEVENSON

O C T O B E R

25	

26	

27	

28	

29	

30/31	*HALLOWEEN*

A solitary maple on a woodside flames in single scarlet, recalls nothing so much as the daughter of a noble house dressed for a fancy ball, with the whole family gathered round to admire her before she goes.

HENRY JAMES

N O V E M B E R

1

2

3

4

5

6

CHOCOLAT

The morns are meeker than they were,
The nuts are getting brown;
The berry's cheek is plumper,
The rose is out of town.

EMILY DICKINSON

NOVEMBER

7

8

9

10

11
VETERANS DAY

12

Fallen leaves lying on the grass in November
bring more happiness than the daffodils.

CYRIL CONNOLLY

NOVEMBER

13

14

15

16

17

18

W e're walking along in the changing-time," said Doe. "Any day now the change will come. It's going to turn from hot to cold . . . . Old Jack Frost will be pinching things up. Old Mr. Winter will be standing in the door. Hickory tree there will be yellow. Sweet-gum red, hickory yellow, dogwood red, sycamore yellow. . . . . Persimmons will all git fit to eat, and the nut will be dropping like rain all through the woods here.

EUDORA WELTY

N O V E M B E R

19

20

21

22

23

24

There is not wind enough to twirl
The one red leaf, the last of its clan,
That dances as often as dance it can,
Hanging so light, and hanging so high,
On the topmost twig that looks up at the sky.

SAMUEL TAYLOR COLERIDGE

NOVEMBER

25

26

27

28

29

30

The whole secret of the study of
Nature lies in learning to use one's eyes. . . .

GEORGE SAND

DECEMBER

1

2

3

4

5

6

'I play for Seasons; not Eternities!'
Says Nature.

GEORGE MEREDITH

D

DECEMBER

7

8

9

10

11

12

In a winter landscape—especially in a wood—
there is the same kind of purity that the Greeks saw in the
unclad human form; it is like a young athlete,
ready for racing, with his flowing garments flung aside.
It is an education in restraint; after seeing it, one cannot
forget the fine severity beneath all natural beauty.

MARY WEBB

DECEMBER

13

14

15

16

17

18

If the world seems cold to you,
Kindle fires to warm it! . . .
If the world's a wilderness,
Go, build houses in it!

LUCY LARCOM

DECEMBER

19	
20	
21	
22	*WINTER SOLSTICE*
23	
24	*CHRISTMAS EVE*

They were spruce! They were birch! They were fir!
Everywhere, everywhere, Christmas tonight!

E. B. WHITE

D E C E M B E R

25	
	CHRISTMAS

26	

27	

28	

29	

30/31	
	NEW YEAR'S EVE

There may be more beautiful times:
but this one is ours.

JEAN-PAUL SARTRE

CREDITS AND ACKNOWLEDGMENTS

Front and back cover and title page "An Idyllic Scene" painting by Eugen Karpathy, courtesy of Fine Arts Photographs & Library Ltd. from Gallerie Berko.

Foreword Photograph by Tina Mucci.

January Excerpt by Albert Camus. Photograph by Toshi Otsuki. Photograph by Katrina. Excerpt from *Taken Care Of* by Edith Sitwell. Photograph by Toshi Otsuki. Photograph by Tina Mucci. Excerpt by Richardson Wright. Photograph by Eric Hanson. Photograph by Starr Ockenga. Excerpt from "Snowbound" by John Greenleaf Whittier. Photograph by Toshi Otsuki. Excerpt from "Frost at Midnight" by Samuel Taylor Coleridge. Photograph by Michael Skott.

February Photograph by Bryan E. McCay. Excerpt from *Raising Demons* by Shirley Jackson. Photograph by John Kane. Photograph by Toshi Otsuki. Excerpt from "A Diary," in *Alphabets and Birthdays*, by Gertrude Stein. Photograph by Toshi Otsuki. Photograph by Starr Ockenga. Excerpt from "Snow-Flakes" by Henry Wadsworth Longfellow. Photograph by Toshi Otsuki. Photograph by Tina Mucci. Excerpt from *Folly* by Susan Minot. Photograph by Toshi Otsuki.

March Photograph by Joan Hix Vanderschuit. Excerpt from "Lines" by William Wordsworth. Photograph by Toshi Otsuki. Excerpt from a letter by Annie Sullivan, quoted in *The Story of My Life* by Helen Keller. Photograph by Toshi Otsuki. Photograph by Steve Cohen. Excerpt from "March—March 1" by Hal Borland. Photograph by Toshi Otsuki. Photograph by Starr Ockenga. Excerpt from the *Essays of E. B. White* by E.B. White. Photograph by Toshi Otsuki. Photograph by Lilo Raymond. Excerpt from . . . *And Ladies of the Club* by Helen Hoover Santmyer. Photograph by Toshi Otsuki.

April Photograph by Tina Mucci. Excerpt from "A Song of Living" by Amelia Josephine Burr. Photograph by Toshi Otsuki. Photograph by Starr Ockenga. Excerpt from "The Woman's Rose" by Olive Schreiner. Photograph by Elyse Lewin. Excerpt from "April" by Sir William Watson. Photograph by Toshi Otsuki. Excerpt from "Green Things Growing" by Dinah Mulock Craik. Photograph by Toshi Otsuki. Photograph by Starr Ockenga. Excerpt from "A Promise-April 29" by Hal Borland. Photograph by Toshi Otsuki.

May Excerpt from "North with the Spring" by Edwin Way Teale. Photograph by Toshi Otsuki. Photograph by Starr Ockenga. Excerpt by Henry David Thoreau. Photograph by Toshi Otsuki. Excerpt from "Spring" by Eliza Cook. Photograph by Bryan E. McCay. Photograph by Bryan E. McCay. Excerpt from "The Goose-Girl" by Edna St. Vincent Millay. Photograph by Toshi Otsuki. Excerpt from *Journal* by Henry Wadsworth Longfellow. Photograph by Toshi Otsuki.

June Photograph by Bryan E. McCay. Excerpt by Gerald Manley Hopkins. Photograph by Toshi Otsuki. Photograph by Tina Mucci. Excerpt by John Constable. Photograph by Toshi Otsuki. Excerpt from "In Early Spring" by Alice Meynell. Photograph by Toshi Otsuki. Photograph by Bryan E. McCay. Excerpt by Lucy Stone, quoted in *Antoinette Brown*

Blackwell: Biographical Sketch by Sarah Gilson. Photograph by Toshi Otsuki. Photograph by Starr Ockenga. Excerpt by Thomas Bailey Aldrich. Photograph by Toshi Otsuki.

July Excerpt by Gérard de Nerval. Photograph by Toshi Otsuki. Photograph by Bryan E. McCay. Photograph by Toshi Otsuki. Photograph by Katrina. Excerpt from the *Essays of E. B. White* by E.B. White. Photograph by Toshi Otsuki. Photograph by Starr Ockenga. Excerpt from "Pretty Lessons in Verse" by Sara Coleridge. Photograph by Hedrich Blessing. Excerpt by Johann Wolfgang von Goethe. Photograph by Tom Arma.

August Photograph by Steve Cohen. Excerpt from "Sunday Morning" by Wallace Stevens. Photograph by Jeff McNamara. Photograph by Steve Gross. Excerpt from *Mad in Pursuit* by Violette Leduc. Photograph by Toshi Otsuki. Photograph by Wendi Schneider. Excerpt from "No. 214" by Emily Dickinson. Photograph by Toshi Otsuki. Excerpt by William Wordsworth. Photograph by Toshi Otsuki. Photograph by Katrina. Excerpt by Colette. Photograph by Toshi Otsuki.

September Photograph by Toshi Otsuki. Photograph by Starr Ockenga. Excerpt from *Some Winchester Letters of Lionel Johnson* by Lionel Johnson. Photograph by Toshi Otsuki. Excerpt from "No. 318" by Emily Dickinson. Photograph by William P. Steele. Photograph by Bryan E. McCay. Photograph by Michael Skott. Photograph by John Jensen. Excerpt from *La Petite Fadette* by George Sand. Photograph by Toshi Otsuki.

October Photograph by Starr Ockenga. Excerpt from "October's Bright Blue Weather" by Helen Hunt Jackson. Photograph from Nina Ovryn Design. Photograph by William P. Steele. Excerpt from *An Unsocial Socialist* by George Bernard Shaw. Photograph by Toshi Otsuki. Excerpt from "The Nightingale" by Samuel Taylor Coleridge. Photograph by Toshi Otsuki. Photograph by Starr Ockenga. Excerpt from *The House Beautiful* by Robert Louis Stevenson. Photograph by Toshi Otsuki. Photograph by Tina Mucci. Excerpt from *The American Scene* by Henry James. Photograph from Nina Ovryn Design.

November Photograph by Toshi Otsuki. Excerpt from "The Morns Are Meeker Than They Were" by Emily Dickinson. Photograph by Toshi Otsuki. Excerpt from *The Unquiet Grave* by Cyril Connolly. Photograph by Toshi Otsuki. Photograph by William P. Steele. Excerpt from "The Wide Net" in *The Wide Net and Other Stories*, by Eudora Welty. Photograph by Toshi Otsuki. Photograph by Starr Ockenga. Excerpt from "Christabel" by Samuel Taylor Coleridge. Photograph by Katrina. Excerpt from *Nouvelles Lettres d'un Voyageur* by George Sand. Photograph from Nina Ovryn Design.

December Excerpt from "Modern Love" by George Meredith. Photograph by Michael Skott. Photograph by Toshi Otsuki. Excerpt from *The Spring of Joy* by Mary Webb. Photograph by John Kane. Photograph by Starr Ockenga. Excerpt from "Three Old Saws" by Lucy Larcom. Photograph by Michael Boys. Excerpt from the *Essays of E.B. White* by E.B. White. Photograph by Toshi Otsuki. Photograph by Konstantin. Excerpt by Jean-Paul Sartre. Photograph by Toshi Otsuki. Photograph by Starr Ockenga.

Endpapers Photograph by Tom Eckerle.